Bible Picture Stories

Published in Great Britain by World Distributors (Manchester) Limited,
P.O. Box 111, 12 Lever Street, Manchester M60 1TS
by arrangement with Western Publishing Company Inc.,
Racine, Wisconsin, U.S.A.

Printed in Italy

SBN 7235 0500 4

Noah Builds the Ark

Genesis 6:5-16

NOAH was a good man who lived many years ago. One day God asked him to build a large boat called an ark.

Noah and his sons worked for many days, cutting down tall trees. How busy they were sawing and hammering! Carefully they pounded each plank in place. The ark grew higher and longer. At last the huge boat was finished. It was very strong. It must sail for many days.

The
Animals
Enter
the Ark

Genesis 6:18-7:6

GOD asked Noah to gather all the animals and birds together. These beasts would live on the ark with Noah and his family.

After a week of hunting, Noah and his sons returned. They guided the beasts, two by two, into the ark. What a noisy place it was! Many strange sounds could be heard. Then Noah and his family went on board. They closed the door and windows. Soon rain began to fall.

Dry Land at Last!

Genesis 8:6-14

NOAH could hear water falling on the roof and splashing against the sides of the ark. The rain continued forty days and forty nights.

Then as suddenly as it had begun, the rain stopped. The sun began to shine. All was quiet. Noah peered out. Water was everywhere! He sent a dove to to find dry land. Once it came back with a small branch in its mouth. Then Noah knew that it had found dry land. The flood was over at last.

The Tower
of Babel

Genesis 11:1-9

LONG ago all people talked and lived alike. But they had become too proud of themselves. They thought they could build a tower which would reach the sky. They made many bricks and laid a foundation. But God did not like their pride. He made them speak many different ways. The people could no longer understand each other. They stopped building the tower. Many moved away. In this way, the nations began.

Rebekah
at the
Well

Genesis 24:1-27

ABRAHAM was an old man far from home. His son, Isaac, was grown up, but he was not married yet. How happy Abraham would be if his son had a wife from his native land! So Abraham sent his most trusted servant to that far country to find a wife for Isaac. When the servant arrived, a pretty young woman offered him and his camels a cool drink of water. Surely this girl would be a good and helpful wife for Isaac. Her name was Rebekah.

Jacob
Deceives
Isaac

Genesis 27:1-29

MANY years passed. Rebekah and Isaac had grown old. Isaac was blind. They had two sons, Jacob and Esau. Esau was older, and this gave him the right to the larger share of his father's property. But Jacob did something wrong. He pretended he was Esau. With animal skins he made his arms feel rough like Esau's. Poor blind Isaac was fooled. He gave Jacob the larger share of his property. This made Esau very angry.

Jacob's Dream

Genesis 28:10-22

JACOB had taken what belonged to his brother, Esau. He decided to run away. He travelled many miles through the desert. Late one night he lay down to sleep. He had a strange dream. He saw steps which seemed to reach to heaven. God was at the top of the steps. Angels walked up and down them. God told Jacob he would give him land and watch over him. In return, Jacob promised part of his possessions to God.

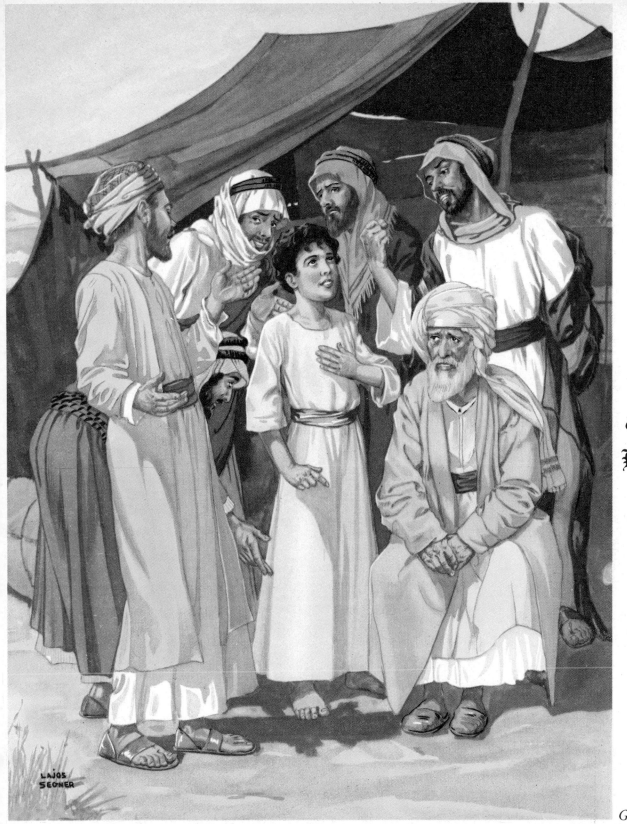

Joseph
and His
Brothers

Genesis 37:3-11

LATER, Jacob settled down to family life. He had twelve sons. Joseph was the favourite. Can you imagine having eleven brothers?

Some of Joseph's brothers did not like him. He had two dreams which made it seem that he was the best in the family. At first, when Joseph told his father and brothers about the dreams, the brothers laughed jealously. They would not believe him. Finally they hated Joseph because of this.

Joseph Explains Pharaoh's Dream

Genesis 37:28;
41:1-14

JOSEPH'S brothers sent him to Egypt as a slave. Before long, he met two servants of Pharaoh, the king. They became good friends.

One night, Pharaoh had a strange vision. Seven good ears of corn were eaten by seven bad ears. And, seven thin cows ate seven fat cows. Pharaoh was bewildered. He asked his wise friends to explain the vision. None could. Then the two servants suggested he send for Joseph.

Storing
the
Grain

Genesis 41:25-41

JOSEPH explained, "There will be seven years of plenty in the land, followed by seven years of want and starvation. You must store up grain during the good years, so your people will have food for the poor years."

Pharaoh thought Joseph was very wise. He asked Joseph to show the men where to put the extra grain. Joseph did this. Later, when hard times came, Joseph and the people of Egypt were prepared.

The Baby
on the
River

Exodus 2:1-10

ONE day the king's daughter went to the river Nile to swim. Suddenly she heard a cry. Near the shore lay a baby in a basket. He had been hidden to protect him from the cruel king. The girl wanted to keep him.

The baby's sister, Miriam, was close by to watch over him. She told the king's daughter she would find a good nurse for the baby. She ran and got her mother. Then she knew her baby brother would be safe.

Moses
Helps
Zipporah

Exodus 2:16-22

THE tiny baby grew up. Moses was his name. As he was hurrying through the desert one day, he came to a well. Seven sisters were trying to water their sheep, but some shepherds had come and tried to drive them away. Moses helped the girls. He watered their sheep for them. One of the sisters invited Moses to their home for supper. Moses fell in love with her. Later they were happily married.

The Burning Bush

Exodus 3:1-12

MOSES was a simple shepherd. He was guiding his flock on the mountain of Horeb, when a strange thing happened. Suddenly a bush began to burn with hot fire. The voice of God called to Moses from the bush.

"You must help the people of Israel. Take them out of Egypt. They are very unhappy there," God said.

Moses was afraid. Could he do this task? But surely God would help.

The
Passover

Exodus 11:4-10;
12:1-28

A dreaded sickness came to the land of Egypt. The first-born child of every family would die from it. But God told Moses in a dream how the people who loved Him could save their little children. One night they were to sacrifice a lamb. Then they were to make marks on the side and above their doors with the blood of the lamb. Any harm would pass over those homes. Even today the people of Israel remember the "passover."

The Escape of the Israelites

Exodus 14:21-31

MOSES' people had to cross the Red Sea to get out of Egypt. As they reached the shore, they could hear the rumble of Pharaoh's mighty army behind them. Then God told Moses to stretch out his hand over the sea. As Moses did this, God sent a strong wind which blew the water away. There was dry land! Quickly the Israelites hurried across between two walls of water. But Pharaoh's men were caught as the water came rushing in again.

Manna
From
Heaven

Exodus 16:13-31

AT last the Israelites were free! How thankful they were to be away from Pharaoh. For many days they wandered in the desert. But before long they began to complain. Their food supply was low. They were afraid they would starve. But Moses told them not to worry. And then the next day, they found food in the desert. God had sent it to them. They called it *manna* from heaven.

Water
for
Thirsty
People

Exodus 17:1-6

IN a few days, the people began to grumble because there was no water. They were very thirsty. They hated the hot, dry sand. Again Moses told them not to worry. He hit some large rocks with his staff, as God told him to do. Water gushed out of the rocks. The people drank the cool clear water. How good it tasted! They filled their pitchers to the brim. They were content once more.

The Ten Command-ments

Exodus 19:1-25; 20:1-17

THE people travelled farther into the desert. One day, they came to some high mountains. Moses told them to wait there until he returned. Then he climbed up the steep rocks. He disappeared from view.

Moses was gone a long time. God spoke the words of the Ten Commandments to him. Then Moses returned. He told the people what God had said. They promised to obey the laws of the commandments.

The Fall of Jericho

*Deuteronomy
31:14
Joshua 6:1-20*

MOSES was old and about to die. He asked young Joshua to lead the Israelites to their new home, their first since they had left Egypt.

To get across the Jordan River, the Israelites would have to fight for the walled city of Jericho. The priests carried the ark, and as the trumpets blared, the walls crumbled to the ground. Joshua's army fought fiercely. The Israelites won! Now they would soon be in their new home.

A
Message
for
Gideon

Judges 6:11-16

MANY years passed. The tribes of Israel were settled in the promised land of Canaan. Next to Canaan lived the people of Midian. Sometimes they stole from the Israelites.

One day a young man named Gideon was busy threshing grain. He hid it in a winepress so the Midianites could not steal it. But an angel came to Gideon and said, "You shall save your people from the Midianites."

Gideon Tests His Soldiers

Judges 7:4-8

GIDEON wondered if he would be able to do as the angel had asked. He immediately called all the men he could rally against the Midianites. Thousands answered the call. But Gideon wanted to test them to see if they were good soldiers. He led them on a march across a brook. Nearly all of them stopped for a long drink. But some only took a small sip of the water. These were the men Gideon thought would be best for the army.

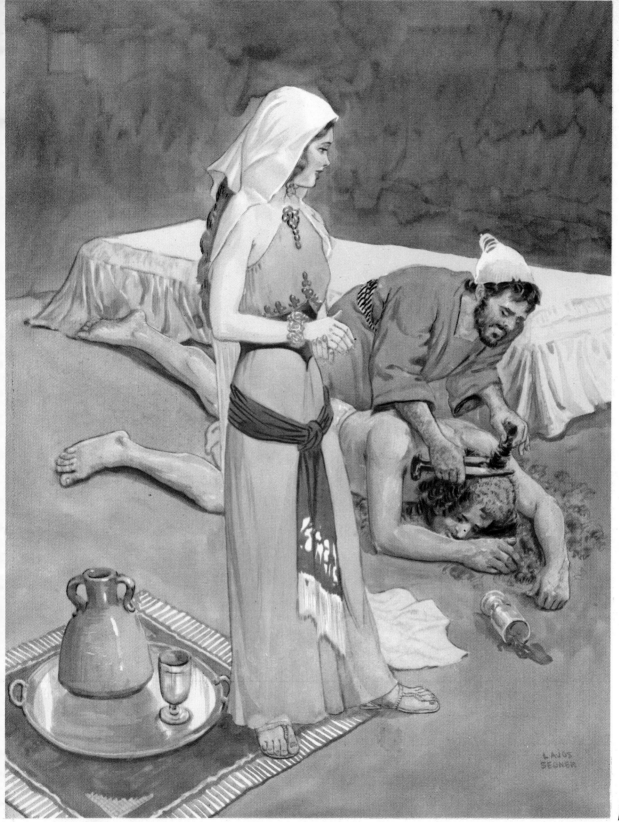

Delilah Betrays Samson

Judges 16:4-18

THE Israelites had another neighbour country which was their enemy. These people were the Philistines. The man whom the Philistines hated most was Samson. He was known everywhere for his tremendous strength. His wife, Delilah, wondered what made him so strong. She often tried to pry his secret from him. At last he told her his hair made him strong. Delilah betrayed Samson. She had his hair cut. He was no longer strong.

Samson in the Mill

Judges 16:18-22

WHEN the Philistines heard this, they rushed after Samson to capture him. Now that his hair was cut, they were sure they would be successful. They were right. Samson's strength had left him. He stood weak and motionless as his enemies tied him up. They put out his eyes. Then they dragged him to the mill to work. There he had to grind corn for the Philistines day after day.

LAJOS SEGNER

Judges 16:22-30

ONE day the Philistines were having a great feast. Some of them remembered Samson. They thought it would be fun to bring him there. They would laugh and jeer at him. But they forgot that Samson's hair had grown again. His strength had returned. As Samson arrived, he silently prayed for more strength. He stood between two pillars. He pulled them with his strong arms and the whole house fell with a crash.

Ruth and Naomi

Ruth 1:1-17

NAOMI was very sad. There had been hunger and sickness in her home. Her husband and her two sons had died.

One day Naomi said to Ruth and Orpha, "You were both faithful wives to my sons. But now you must go to your own homes in Moab."

Orpha kissed Naomi good-by. But Ruth put her arms around Naomi and promised she would never leave her.

Ruth and Boaz

*Ruth 1:18-22;
3:1-18; 4:1-10*

LATER they went to Bethlehem, Naomi's old home. A relative of her husband's lived there too. He was a farmer named Boaz.

Soon after Ruth and Naomi arrived, Ruth decided she would like to help Boaz harvest the grain. She worked very hard. Boaz noticed this. At lunchtime he sat beside Ruth and shared his food with her. Before long they found they loved each other. Later they were married.

Samuel Enters the Temple

I Samuel 1:8-28

IN the quiet of the temple, Eli the priest watched a woman pray. Finally she looked up. She told him she was praying for a baby son.

Several years later, the woman again came to the temple. She had a small boy with her. She said to Eli, "I am the woman who was here before. God answered my prayer. I have brought you my son Samuel."

And Samuel stayed to help Eli in the temple.

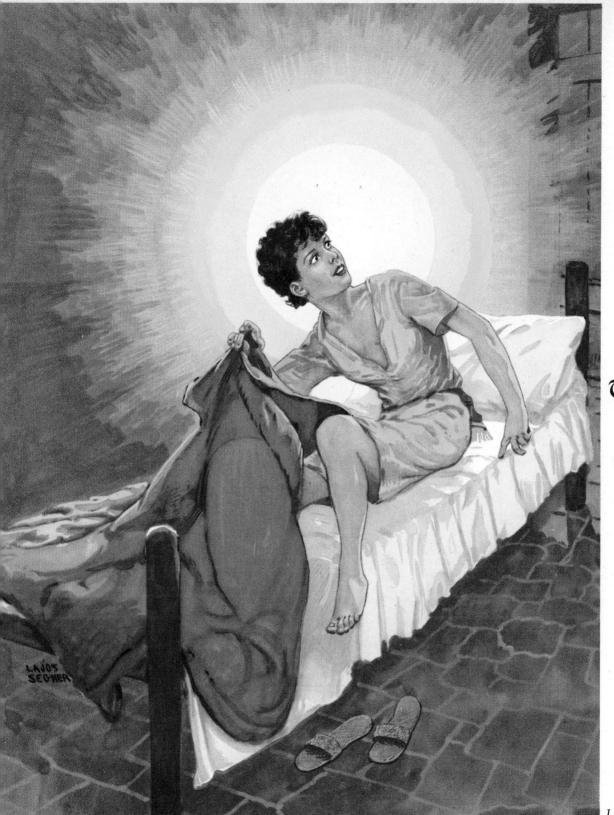

The Call
to
Samuel

I Samuel 3:1-18

ONE night Samuel and Eli lay sleeping. Suddenly Samuel awoke with a start. Someone was calling his name. He thought it was Eli. But the priest told him he had not called. After this had happened three times, Eli said, "It is the Lord who is calling to you. Listen and tell me what message he has for you."

And Samuel listened and told Eli all that God had said.

Samuel Anoints Saul

I Samuel 7:15-17;
8:1-9; 9:1-21;10:1

MANY years had passed since Samuel had heard God's call. He had been a faithful priest after Eli died, but now the people wanted a king. Samuel felt a king would not be best for them. However, he found a fine young man named Saul to rule the people.

Samuel anointed Saul with oil and entrusted him with the high office of king of the people.

Jonah and
the Whale

*Jonah 1:1-5, 9-17;
2:1-10*

THE boat to Joppa tossed wildly on the stormy sea. The frightened sailors thought there must be some reason for this terrible storm. Then they found a passenger named Jonah, who confessed he was running away from a job God had asked him to do. Jonah was thrown overboard and the storm stopped. Then he was swallowed by a whale. Later, when Jonah promised to do what God had asked, he found himself safe on dry land again.

The Courage of David

I Samuel 17:34-36

ONE summer day, a young shepherd boy was guarding his flock. David was his name. As he was sitting on the grass enjoying the warm sunshine, he heard an angry roar. Suddenly, from behind some rocks, leaped a huge lion. Quickly David grabbed his sling. He took careful aim and threw the stone. The lion fell dead. David had saved his sheep. David was a brave boy and soon even Samuel and King Saul heard of the boy's courage.

David
and
Goliath

I Samuel 17:1-50

ABOUT this time, the Philistines made war on the Israelites. Among the Philistines was a man named Goliath. He was very tall and strong. He wore a suit of armor and carried a long sword. The Israelites were very frightened. How could they kill a big man like this? Then David heard about Goliath. He was not afraid. Swiftly he shot a stone from his sling. It did not miss. Goliath fell to the ground and everybody cheered.

David
Sings
to Saul

I Samuel 18:6-9;
16:23

THE war between the Philistines and the Israelites ended. The people thought David was a wonderful hero. They hailed him everywhere. When King Saul heard of this, he became angry. But music seemed to make him feel better. Now David could play the harp and sing beautifully. In spite of his growing hatred for David, King Saul often asked David to sing and play for him. King Saul did not feel so sad then.

True
Friends

*I Samuel
18:28-30;
19:1-7*

MORE and more, the Israelites seemed to like David. This made King Saul more and more jealous. Why, even his own son Jonathan was a good friend of David's. He must destroy this young enemy!

When Jonathan heard of his father's hatred and plotting, he ran to David and warned him to hide. When King Saul planned to kill David, it was Jonathan who saved his life. Surely he was a true friend.

Solomon's Temple

I Kings 5:1-18;
6:1-38

AFTER King Saul's death, David was anointed king. Some of his years as ruler of the people were happy and some were sad. Finally after being king for forty years, David died. Then his son, Solomon, reigned. Solomon was a very wise man, though he loved riches and often forgot God. One thing he did was to build a beautiful temple in Jerusalem. It was made of cedar wood, marble, and gold. Solomon's temple was very beautiful.

Food for
Elijah

I Kings 17:3-7

YEARS passed. Many cruel and selfish kings reigned after Solomon. The people had a hard life. There were wars and hardships and the people came to worship idols instead of God.

Then God sent a prophet named Elijah. He was poor. Often he had no food, but God sent bread with the ravens, for Elijah was a good man and he loved God.

A Cake for Elijah

I Kings 17:9-16

No rain had fallen for many days. The farmers' fields were burned. Even the brook near where Elijah lived had dried up. Then God told him to go to a certain small town. There he would find a woman who would give him food. Elijah met a woman and asked her to make a cake for herself and her son and for him. She had very little meal left, but Elijah told her she would have enough, for God had promised him this.

I Kings 17:17-24

God
Answers
Elijah's
Prayer

ONE day the little boy of the house became ill. His mother was afraid he would die. Because of this she wondered if Elijah had been sent to punish her for her wrong doings.

"Give me your son," Elijah said. Then he carried the boy upstairs. Gently he laid him on the bed. He prayed earnestly. And God made the boy well again. Then his mother knew that Elijah was a man of God.

Elisha's Vision

I Kings 19:19-21
II Kings 2:1-11

OLD Elijah knew he must find someone to take his place. His work was almost done. Then one day as he was walking to the city, he saw a young man plowing a field. Elisha was his name. Elijah asked him to be his helper. They worked together. Not long after this, Elisha saw a fiery chariot which seemed to come down from the sky. He fell on his knees as he saw Elijah being taken up to heaven. The old prophet was gone.

The
Healing
of
Naaman

II Kings 5:1-14

ELISHA was left to carry on. He did much to help people.

Naaman was a soldier in the Syrian army. He was sick with leprosy. Someone said that perhaps the king could cure him. Of course the king could not, but Elisha could. He told Naaman to bathe in the Jordan River seven times. At first Naaman refused, but finally he did as Elisha said. Then he was cured. It was a miracle!

Three Brave Men

Daniel 3:1-30

NEBUCHADNEZZAR, the king, had a huge golden image built. He ordered his people to worship this idol. Anyone who did not do as he asked, would be punished. Shadrach, Meshach, and Abednego were brave enough to refuse to worship the idol, for they believed in God. The king had them thrown into a fiery furnace. But they were not burned. When the king saw this, he knew that their God was the only true God.

mene
mene
tekel
upharsin

Daniel 5:1-31

NEBUCHADNEZZAR'S son became king. One night he was entertaining thousands of people at a great feast. Suddenly he was startled! What was this? A hand, writing on the wall! Terrified, the king asked what it meant. Then Daniel came forward and said, "The great empire of your father has grown smaller. You have been a poor leader. Your kingdom will soon be divided by the Persians." And Daniel was right.

Daniel in the Lions' Den

Daniel 6:1-22

DANIEL was not afraid, even though he was to be thrown into the lions' den. He knew he had done nothing really wrong. He had only worshiped God in his usual way. But that was against the king's orders.

The next day, the worried king peered into the den. There sat Daniel beside the quiet lions. He was not hurt! His God had protected him. This God, the king thought, was a truly great God!